# CASEY
# AT THE BAT

Casey at the Bat

This edition published by Rand McNally & Company, 1985

Library of Congress Number: 85-61533
Printed in Italy

# CASEY AT THE BAT

Ernest Lawrence Thayer
Illustrated by Ken Bachaus

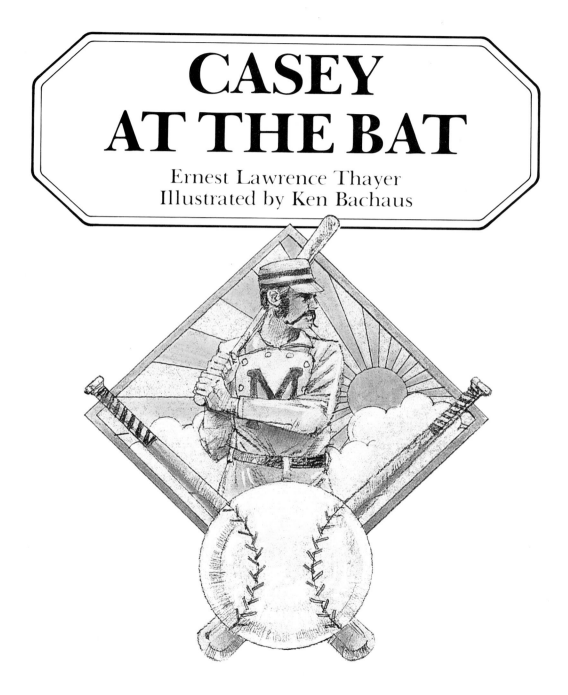

**Rand McNally & Company**
Chicago · New York · San Francisco

The outlook wasn't brilliant
for the Mudville nine that day:
The score stood four to two
with but one inning more to play.

| | 1 | 2 | 3 | 4 | 5 | 6 | 7 | 8 | 9 | R | H | E |
|---|---|---|---|---|---|---|---|---|---|---|---|---|
| VISITORS | 0 | 1 | 0 | 2 | 0 | 0 | 0 | 1 | 0 | 4 | 9 | 1 |
| HOME | 0 | 0 | 1 | 0 | 0 | 0 | 1 | 0 | | 2 | 7 | 3 |

And then when Cooney died at first,
    and Barrows did the same,
A sickly silence fell
    upon the patrons of the game.

A straggling few got up
  to go in deep despair. The rest
Clung to that hope which springs eternal
  in the human breast;
They thought if only Casey
  could but get a whack at that—
We'd put up even money now
  with Casey at the bat.

B ut Flynn preceded Casey,
as did also Jimmy Blake,
And the former was a lulu
and the latter was a cake;
So upon that stricken multitude
grim melancholy sat.
For there seemed but little chance
of Casey's getting to the bat.

But Flynn let drive a single,
   to the wonderment of all,
And Blake, the much despis-ed,
   tore the cover off the ball;
And when the dust had lifted,
   and the men saw what had occurred,
There was Jimmy safe at second
   and Flynn a-hugging third.

Then from 5,000 throats and more
 there rose a lusty yell;
It rumbled through the valley,
 it rattled in the dell;
It knocked upon the mountain
 and recoiled upon the flat,
For Casey, mighty Casey,
 was advancing to the bat.

There was ease in Casey's manner
  as he stepped into his place;
There was pride in Casey's bearing
  and a smile on Casey's face.
And when, responding to the cheers,
  he lightly doffed his hat,
No stranger in the crowd could doubt
  'twas Casey at the bat.

Ten thousand eyes were on him
    as he rubbed his hands with dirt;
Five thousand tongues applauded
    when he wiped them on his shirt.
Then while the writhing pitcher
    ground the ball into his hip,
Defiance gleamed in Casey's eye,
    a sneer curled Casey's lip.

And now the leather-covered sphere
  came hurtling through the air,
And Casey stood a-watching it
  in haughty grandeur there.
Close by the sturdy batsman
  the ball unheeded sped—
"That ain't my style," said Casey.
  "Strike one," the umpire said.

From the benches, black with people,
   there went up a muffled roar,
Like the beating of the storm-waves
   on a stern and distant shore.
"Kill him! Kill the umpire!"
   shouted someone on the stand;
And it's likely they'd have killed him
   had not Casey raised his hand.

With a smile of Christian charity
  great Casey's visage shone;
He stilled the rising tumult;
  he bade the game go on;
He signaled to the pitcher,
  and once more the spheroid flew;
But Casey still ignored it,
  and the umpire said, "Strike two."

"Fraud!" cried the maddened thousands,
    and echo answered fraud;
But one scornful look from Casey
    and the audience was awed.
They saw his face grow stern and cold,
    they saw his muscles strain,
And they knew that Casey
    wouldn't let that ball go by again.

The sneer is gone from Casey's lip,
  his teeth are clenched in hate;
He pounds with cruel violence
  his bat upon the plate.
And now the pitcher holds the ball,
  and now he lets it go,
And now the air is shattered
  by the force of Casey's blow.

Oh, somewhere in this favored land
   the sun is shining bright;
The band is playing somewhere,
   and somewhere hearts are light,
And somewhere men are laughing,
   and somewhere children shout;

But there is no joy in Mudville—
mighty Casey has struck out.